This edition printed in the United Kingdom, 2020

ISBN: 978-1-5272-5557-9

LITTLE
HONEY BEE

Written and illustrated by Aimee Ogden

Out in the field, under the moon, creatures were snoozing and snoring away.

But something, somewhere, was making a strange sniffling sound.

"What's wrong Little Honey Bee?"

"On my journey I have found animals that are...

FASTER

And others that are
BIGGER

There are creatures that are
STRONGER

There are those that are

TALLER

There are some that are

WISER

"Mr Owl, please can you
show me the way home?"

And I just feel so...

small. I'm not important."

"Now Little Honey Bee,
let me tell you a secret.
It's most important
that you remember."

The honey bee visits between 50 to 100 flowers during it's journey.

A powerful sniffer - can tell if a flower has pollen from metres away.

Even though they have small brains, they have the ability to learn and make difficult decisions.

The perks of being a honey bee.

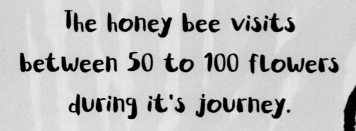

Transfers pollen between male and female flowers which means that plants can grow seeds and fruit.

Their wings beat at around 200 beats per second. This is what creates the buzzing sound.

Communicates with other honey bees by dancing.

A hive will fly 90,000 miles = 3 trips around the world.

Honey is the only food that includes all the substances that are needed to keep people and creatures alive.

"You are important
because you are you.

You do a work that no
other creature can do.

You don't have to look far
to know it's the truth;
all these things are alive
and happy because of you."

A warm feeling could be felt in
Little Honey Bee's heart because
what Papa bee said was true;

"It's okay to not be the fastest, or the biggest, or the strongest or the tallest, or even the wisest.

You are enough just being you."